Ransom Neutron Stars
In the Stars
by Alice Hemming
Illustrated by Tania Vicedo

Published by Ransom Publishing Ltd.
Unit 7, Brocklands Farm, West Meon, Hampshire GU32 1JN, UK
www.ransom.co.uk

ISBN   978 178591 443 0
First published in 2017
Reprinted 2018

A CIP catalogue record of this book is available from the British Library.

There is a reading comprehension quiz available for this book in the popular
Accelerated Reader® software system. For information about ATOS, Accelerated
Reader, quiz points and reading levels please visit www.renaissance.com. Accelerated
Reader, AR, the Accelerated Reader Logo, and ATOS are trademarks of Renaissance
Learning, Inc. and its subsidiaries, registered common law or applied for in the U.S.
and other countries. Used under license.

In the Stars

Alice Hemming

Illustrated by Tania Vicedo

Ransom

I am on my own.

Just my cat and I.

At night we look at the stars.

Just my cat and I.

There are about 100 billion stars in our galaxy.

Our galaxy is big.

I am small.

My problems are small.

I am just one lonely man
on a great big planet.

11

The stars never look the same.

They move and change.

They have different colours
and different patterns.

13

I see amazing things, but I have
nobody to talk to.

Only my cat.

Tonight I see a strange light in the sky.
It is bright.

"Is that a comet?" I say to the cat.

I need a bigger telescope.

There is a bigger telescope
at the Astronomy Centre.

I drive to the Centre in my car.

It is night.

The Astronomy Centre is nearly empty.

One person is here. She is looking through the big telescope.

I wait.

"Sorry. Did you wait long?" she says.

"No," I say.

"I saw something odd in the sky," she says. "It has gone now."

"May I look?" I say.

I look through the big telescope.
I can see nothing.

Maybe there was nothing to see.

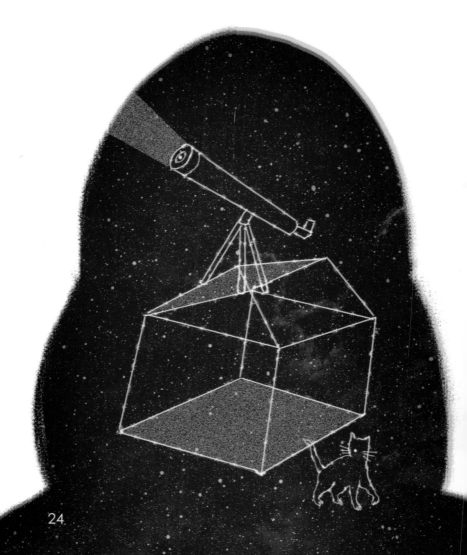

"I am Sara," she says.

"It is just me at home. Me and my cat," she says. "Every night we look at the stars."

"I have a cat, too," I say. "Every night I look at the stars with my cat. Sometimes I want to talk about the stars."

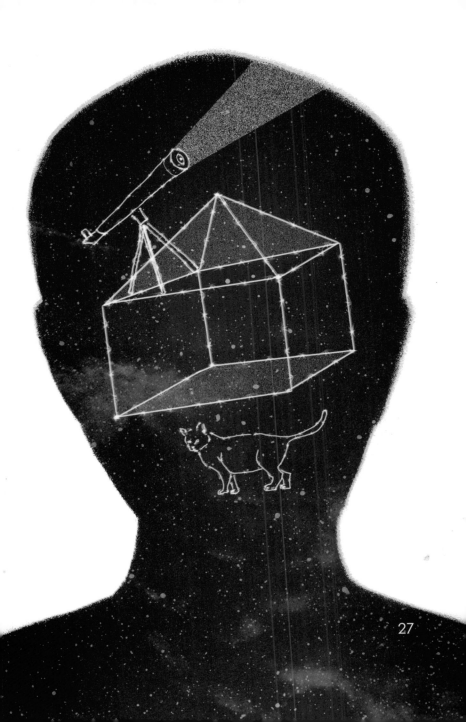

"Me too," Sara says. "Let's have a coffee. We can talk."

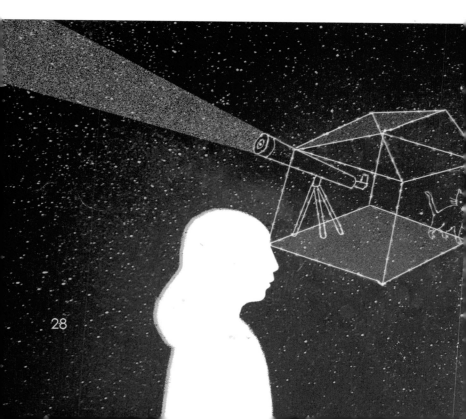

Sara has a flask of hot coffee. We find two cups.

I have a picnic rug.

It is a warm night. We sit outside on the rug.

We talk all evening.

The stars move above us.

We are just two lonely people
on a great big planet.

Some things are meant to be.

It's in the stars!

Ransom Neutron Stars

In the Stars
Word count **310**

Yellow Book Band

Phonics

Phonics 1 Not Pop, Not Rock Go to the Laptop Man Gus and the Tin of Ham	*Phonics 2* Deep in the Dark Woods Night Combat Ben's Jerk Chicken Van
Phonics 3 GBH Steel Pan Traffic Jam Platform 7	*Phonics 4* The Rock Show Gaps in the Brain New Kinds of Energy

Book bands

Pink Curry! Free Runners My Toys	*Red* Shopping with Zombies Into the Scanner Planting My Garden
Yellow Fit for Love The Lottery Ticket **In the Stars**	*Blue* Awesome ATAs Wolves The Giant Jigsaw
Green Fly, May FLY! How to Start Your Own Crazy Cult The Care Home	*Orange* Text Me The Last Soldier Best Friends